# The Great Big Enormous Turnip

## by Alexei Tolstoy

SCOTT, FORESMAN AND COMPANY • GLENVIEW, ILLINOIS
Dallas, Tex. • Oakland, N.J. • Palo Alto, Cal. • Tucker, Ga. • Brighton, England

ISBN 0-673-10624-1

# The Great Big Enormous Turnip

Once upon a time an old man planted a little turnip.

The old man said,
"Grow, grow, little turnip.
Grow sweet.
Grow, grow, little turnip.
Grow strong."

3

And the turnip grew up sweet and strong and big and enormous.

Then one day the old man went to
pull it up.
He pulled—and pulled again.
But he could not pull it up.

The old man called the old woman.
He said, "Come and help with
the turnip."

The old woman pulled the old man.
The old man pulled the turnip.
And they pulled—and pulled again.
But they could not pull it up.

The old woman called her granddaughter.
She said, "Come and help with
the turnip."

14

The granddaughter pulled the old woman.
The old woman pulled the old man.
The old man pulled the turnip.
And they pulled—and pulled again.
But they could not pull it up.

The granddaughter called the black dog. She said, "Come and help with the turnip."

The black dog pulled the granddaughter.
The granddaughter pulled the old woman.
The old woman pulled the old man.
The old man pulled the turnip.
And they pulled—and pulled again.
But they could not pull it up.

38

The black dog called the cat.
She said, "Come and help with
the turnip."

14

The cat pulled the dog.
The dog pulled the granddaughter.
The granddaughter pulled the old woman.
The old woman pulled the old man.
The old man pulled the turnip.
And they pulled—and pulled again.
But still they could not pull it up.

The cat called the mouse.
He said, "Come and help with
the turnip."

13

The mouse pulled the cat.
The cat pulled the dog.
The dog pulled the granddaughter.
The granddaughter pulled the old woman.
The old woman pulled the old man.
The old man pulled the turnip.
They pulled—and pulled again.

39

And up came the turnip at last!

# Turnips

Turnips grow in gardens.
The roots grow in the ground.
They are white.

The leaves of turnips are green.
They grow above the ground.
The leaves are called greens.

Turnips and greens are sold in stores.
They are good to eat.

Turnips and greens are good when
they are cooked.

Raw turnips and greens are good too.

# The Turnip Song

Words and music by Uncle Don

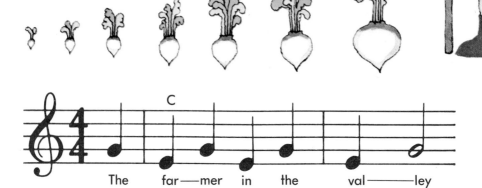

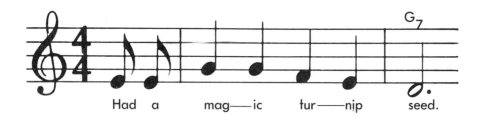

The far—mer in the val———ley

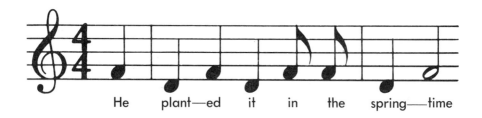

Had a mag—ic tur—nip seed.

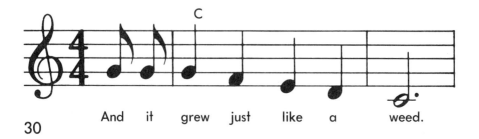

He plant—ed it in the spring—time

And it grew just like a weed.

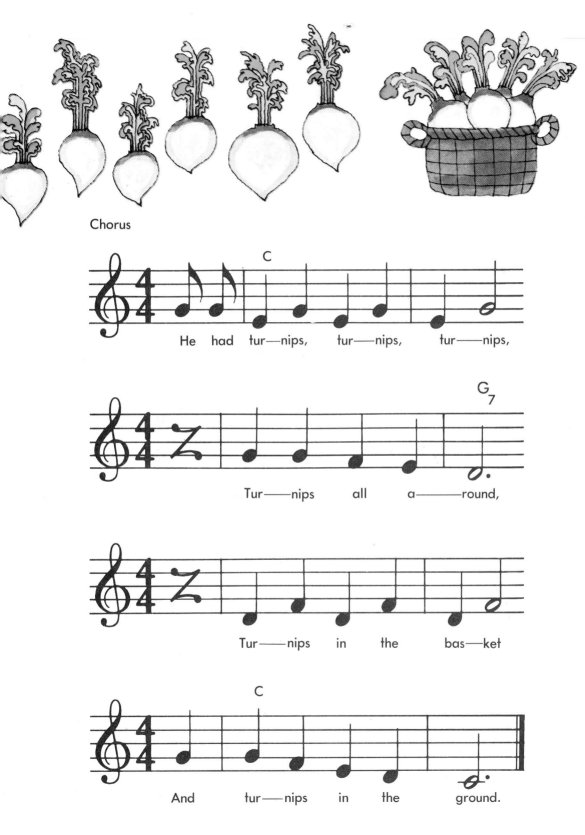

Chorus

He had tur—nips, tur—nips, tur—nips,

Tur—nips all a——round,

Tur——nips in the bas—ket

And tur—nips in the ground.

There were turnips in the barnyard.
There were turnips in the hay.
There were turnips in the orchard
And more grew every day.

Repeat the chorus.

He ate turnips for his dinner.
He ate turnips for his lunch.
He ate turnips for his supper
And even Sunday brunch.

Repeat the chorus.